Contents

Special Features

 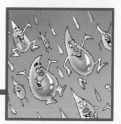
Features

Look Through the Window

Written by Matthew Dunstan

Look through the window.

The sky is blue,
but today it is cold outside.
It is too cold
to go outside to play.

Look through the window.

The wind is blowing,
and today it is cold outside.
It is too cold
to go outside to play.

Look through the window.

It is raining,
and today it is cold outside.
It is too cold
to go outside to play.

Look through the window.

There is snow on the ground.
It is cold.
Today, it is too cold
to go outside to play.

Look through the window.

There is ice on the grass.
It is cold.
Today, it is too cold
to go outside to play.

Look through the window.

There are blossoms on the trees,
but today it is cold outside.
It is too cold
to go outside to play.

Look through the window.

The children are outside.
Today, it is not too cold
to go outside to play.

Safari WORD POWER

 Aa
 Bb
 **Cc**
 **Dd**
 **Ee**
 **Ff**
 Gg
Hh
Ii

 **Zz**
 Yy
 **Xx**
 **Ww**
 **Vv**
 **Uu**
 Tt
 Ss
 Rr

through

outside

under

play

but

today

Find –
but   outside   play
through   today   under

 **Jj**
 **Kk**
 Ll
 Mm
 Nn
 Oo
 Pp
 Qq

Rain, Rain, Go Away!

Traditional

Illustrated by Carol Herring

Rain, Rain,
Go away!
Come again
Another day!

Rain, Rain,
Go away,
So we can go
Outside to play!

again
chain
gain
grain
pain
plain
rain

again
chain
gain
grain
pain
plain
rain

again
chain
gain
grain
pain
plain
rain

again
chain
gain
grain
pain
plain
rain

The Rain Comes Down

Written by Jan McPherson
Illustrated by Jane Macdonald

Rain falls.
It falls from the sky
and onto the roof.

The rain falls.
It falls onto the roof
and runs down
the drainpipe.

The rain falls.
It runs down the drainpipe
and into the drain.

The rain falls.
The water runs into the drain,
under the garden,
and under the street.

The water runs under the street and into the stream.

The rain falls and falls.

The Raindrops

Written by Krystal Diaz

Illustrated by Richard Hoit

Rachel Raindrop

Rebecca Raindrop

Rick Raindrop

Ryan Raindrop

Rick

We are going to fall down
to the ground today.

Rachel

I like falling down to the ground.
I like falling fast.

Ryan

Will we make a lot of rain
or a little rain today?

Rebecca

We are going to make
a little rain today.

Rachel

I like falling fast.
I like making a lot of rain.

Rick

No. We are going to make
a little rain. We do not want
to make a flood.

Ryan

We made a flood last week.

Rebecca

We do not want
to make a flood this week.
The ground is still very wet.

Rachel

I like making a lot of rain.
I like falling down to the ground fast.

Rick

You cannot fall down
to the ground fast today.
You cannot make a lot of rain.

Ryan

Today we are going to make
a little rain.
And that is that!

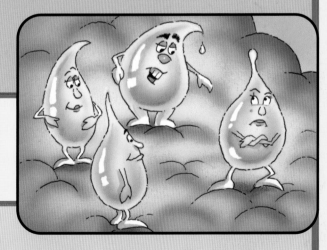

Rachel

I am going to go fast. Here I go!

Rebecca
No one will know it is raining.
No one will know
that Rachel Raindrop
has fallen down to the ground.

Rick
We will go down
to the ground now.
We will make a little rain.

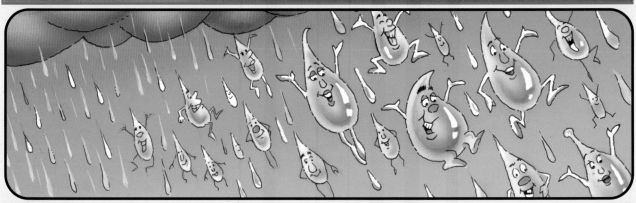

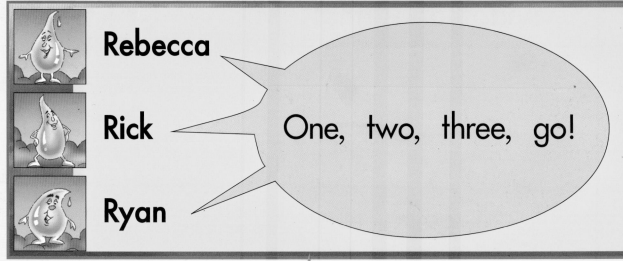

Rebecca

Rick

Ryan

One, two, three, go!

It's Raining

Written by Maria Kennedy

It's raining on the mailbox.
It's raining on the dog.
It's raining on the lily pads.
It's raining on the frog.

It's raining on the sand.
It's raining on the sea.
It's raining on the umbrella,
But not on me!

readingsafari.com

Check out these Safari magazines, too!

Have your say -

e-mail your Safari Tour Guide at
tourguide@readingsafari.com

Safari Tour Guide, **40**

I wrote a story about a big storm.
Do you want me to send it to you?

Winona Ridge (6)

Find some fun things to do!

Go to –
http://www.readingsafari.com

Safari *Superstar*

Name – Rebecca Raindrop

Birthday – August 8

Find out more about this
Safari Superstar at
http://www.readingsafari.com